MAKE YOUR OWN
CLASSIC SPORTS CARS

Model engineering by Pat Doyle
Colour artwork by Inkwell Studios
Other illustrations by Pat Doyle and Steve West
Text by Karen Farrington and Nick Constable

Cars come in all shapes and sizes, fast or slow, sleek or square, luxury or basic. Only 100 years ago the first cars were feared and loathed as nuisances on the road, but now there are about 480 million vehicles used worldwide, and they are a vital part of daily life, taking people to and from work and to visit their relatives and friends.

THE FIRST CARS

Cars – or 'horse-less carriages' as they were first known – were created in the age of steam. In 1771, Frenchman Nicolas Cugnot built a bulky iron-and-wood three-wheeler which was christened 'the fardier'. A water-filled boiler at the front was heated by fire to make steam which worked pistons in adjoining cylinders. It wasn't designed to carry people but to pull a hefty gun for the army. They were built throughout the 19th century with varying degrees of success.

In Britain, the production of steam cars was all but halted by the Locomotive Act of 1865, which declared that all mechanically operated road vehicles should travel no faster than four miles per hour on the open road or two miles per hour in the town. Each vehicle was supposed to have a crew of three, a driver, a stoker and a man to walk ahead waving a red flag or lamp by way of warning.

The development of the car carried on elsewhere in the world. The best steam cars were built in America at the turn of the century. They were known as Stanleys. A Stanley called the *Wogglebug* set an unofficial world record with a speed of 204 km (127 miles) per hour in 1906.

Then came the invention of the internal combustion engine, that is, when the fuel is burned inside the engine cover rather than outside like a steam engine; but it wasn't until the innovation of the petrol-driven engine that cars seemed to have a future.

It is thanks to two German engineers working alone, but situated only a matter of 96 km (60 miles) apart from each other, that the motor car became as popular as it is today.

Nicolas Cugnot's Fardier was very hard to steer and equally hard to stop.

Daimler taking a friend for a drive.

One of these German inventors was called Gottlieb Daimler who in 1885, after spending long hours in a garden workshop, unveiled a contraption called a four-stroke engine. The following year he attached a refined version of it to the underside of a carriage made for horses, to create the first car. A local newspaper decided it was 'diabolical and dangerous to life'.

The other inventor was called Karl Benz. He mounted his engine beneath the seat of a three-wheeled body complete with rubber tyres and a bicycle chain. The fuel he used was benzine which was ignited by battery, coil and a hand-made spark plug. Although it boasted a hand-brake, the vehicle was driven by a steering lever rather than a wheel.

It crashed on its first run, to the joy of assembled sceptics, but Benz knew it showed promise. So did his wife Bertha, who put her husband's jalopy to the test in 1888 when she set out for a 80 kms (50 miles) journey with her two sons and completed it successfully inside a day. This first dream machine is today in a museum in Munich.

Still, not everyone was convinced. And both men had trouble finding cash backers who would invest in production of bigger and better models. The first vehicles that went up for sale didn't attract a single customer. By 1891 Benz had designed and made a four-wheel car called the Viktoria and this excited a bit more interest. Finally a lighter, cheaper model called the 'Velo' which travelled at little more than 19 km (12 miles) per hour scored some significant success. In 1895 there were a total of 111 Benz cars on the roads of Europe.

A spate of accidents, which inevitably happened, set many people against cars in the early days. The first fatal road accident came on 13 September 1895, when a Mr W. H. Bliss was knocked down in New York. In Britain the first victim came a year later on 17 August 1896, when Mrs Bridget Driscoll was killed at Crystal Palace, South London. In 1897 an accident victim in Paris told his local police chief he was going to get a pistol and shoot any driver who came his way.

Fortunately the crisis was averted, but for many years German and British drivers were expected to stop for horses to pass. The saddle-bound gentry of the day were furious when their animals bolted or reared when frightened by a car – until they themselves became car owners.

Other designers were excited by the idea of cars, most notably in France and Italy. Many improved on the engine or the design, but the principle of motor transport was established by trail-blazers Daimler and Benz.

Daimler Benz also made a three-wheeler.

FAMOUS CAR MANUFACTURERS

Ferrari

The man behind the prancing horse, symbol of this swish motor, was Enzo Ferrari. He was born in 1898, and when he saw his first road race at the age of 10, he vowed to become a racing driver. At 13 he mastered the cumbersome gears fitted to all cars of the day, and soon took a job as a test driver. Within a matter of months he was racing for Alfa Romeo, the car company which had been producing prestige vehicles since 1909. He went on to become manager of its racing team.

Ferrari finally split from Alfa Romeo to start his own business in 1946, by which time he was already associated with the black horse emblem. Parents of a First World War fighter pilot had given him a piece of their son's shattered aeroplane in 1923 which bore the horse design. It appeared on his team's winning cars, proving something of a lucky charm. At first, Ferraris were designed only for racing but they soon found a place among the connoisseurs of everyday motoring.

His company boasted of having in its stable what was then the world's most powerful car, the Ferrari 375 Millemiglia. Enzo died in 1988 after seeing the F40 produced, the first road car capable of 320 km (200 miles) per hour. Today the brand name is owned by Italian auto giant Fiat. Ferraris are still known as the world's most expensive second-hand cars, with some models reaching millions of pounds at auction.

A Ferrari racing car of the 1950s.

The Porsche, type 356A, Super 75 1600 cc form.

Porsche

Ferdinand Porsche was born in Austria, in 1875. His first association with cars came through Gottlieb Daimler's company where he worked until 1931. Then Porsche decided to design sports and racing cars independently. A few years later, in association with Hitler, he got to work on a 'people's car' with his son Ferdinand, known as Ferry. In 1934 he proudly showed off his triumph, the Volkswagen or 'Beetle'. The lovingly moulded curves and endearing character of the car wins hearts even today.

After the Second World War, Porsche was jailed by the French as punishment for his long-time association with the evil German leader. It was left to Ferry to raise a massive ransom to secure his father's release, which he did by helping to design a Grand Prix car called the Cisitalia. The first Porsche sports car was made in 1944, using parts similar to those found in its 'poor relation', the Beetle. In it, the driver sat in front of the engine.

This remains a design feature of Porsches today. Without an engine under the bonnet, the nose of the car is thinner and more streamlined.

Lamborghini

Ferruccio Lamborghini made his fortune in tractor manufacturing and central heating, but he was something of a car fanatic, and grew dissatisfied with the Ferraris he had been driving. He felt sure he could build a better road car, and assembled a top team of designers to do just that. The result was the Lamborghini 350GT, first produced in 1963, a car with revolutionary twin overhead camshafts giving it a top speed of 270 km (168 miles) per hour. It also boasted superior suspension and steel bodywork.

A series of sleek road cars were produced in the following decade, until the most stunning car of his series was unveiled in 1971. The Countach was a wedge-shaped supercar with doors that opened up like wings. When it was produced for the first time three years later, it was acclaimed as 'king of the road', a title some award it to this day.

Lamborghini Countach.

Ford

American Henry Ford first produced cars in 1903. Thanks to him, cars became available to more people than ever. He mass-produced vehicles, which drastically cut their cost. He chose to concentrate on the Model T and had an army of men, each doing a specialised job, to get as many off the production line as he could in the shortest possible time. In 1909 over 10,500 were built (more than his rivals could manage), all of which were black in colour. By 1913 he had hit on moving conveyor belts to bring even more speed to the process. But the car was considered rather cheap by the snobs of the day, who nicknamed it the 'Tin Lizzie'. Ford himself chuckled at the jibes aimed at his car, including the joke: 'What's the time when two Fords pass one another? Tin past tin.'

Of course, he had the last laugh. An astonishing 15 million Model T's were sold between 1908 and 1927 when production ceased. By the time he died in 1947, he saw the system he pioneered for car production in use worldwide.

Rolls-Royce 'The Silver Ghost', in production from 1907.

Rolls Royce

The first car owned by Englishman Henry Royce was a French Decauville made in 1901. Unimpressed, he felt sure he could make a better one himself. Borrowing from the Decauville design, he worked on his own car, which he road tested for the first time in 1904. It was instantly obvious his model was a superior type model, reliable, quiet and a treat to drive. The car captured the imagination of the aristocrat Charles Rolls, who went into partnership with Royce to make and market the cars.

The first noted model made by the pair came in 1906. It was the famous Silver Ghost, named because it ran so quietly. Before long it earned the accolade of 'The best car in the world'. Rolls turned his attention to flying but, unfortunately, became the first Englishman to be killed in a flying accident.

Royce, suffering poor health due to years of overwork, retired to a villa in Southern France where he continued to design cars. Claude Johnson, who had long been associated with the company, took over the helm. It was he who set up a base in America and also pushed for the superb Rolls-Royce engines to be used in planes.

JAPAN, THE RISING SUN

In 1956, Japan exported just 46 cars. In 1960 they produced only 1.3 per cent of the world's cars. Soon after, they began to copy successful Western designs, producing them efficiently and cheaply. As their confidence grew, they began to stamp on their own distinctive design. By 1973, Japanese car makers Datsun made 1 in 20 of all cars sold in Britain.

Today, millions of Japanese cars are sent overseas, while many more are produced in factories around the world. The key to the country's success is the use of highly technical machinery which is in action on the production lines. The robot arms, introduced in 1970, not only cut costs by saving labour but also produce a reliable, well-made machine.

HOW CARS WORK

Usually, a car has four wheels. Most of today's models have the front two driven by the engine – hence the phrase two-wheel drive. Four-wheel drive vehicles are generally more expensive, but offer exceptional roadholding in tough conditions, like deserts and farms.

Most cars have a four-stroke internal combustion engine. That means there are four actions in the engine cycle which generates power; the first draws in fuel and air; the second moves up to compress the fuel and air mixture; the third ignites it, and the fourth ejects waste gases. The stages are known as induction, compression, ignition and exhaust. Petrol arrives in the engine from the fuel tank, via the carburettor, which converts it into a gas.

Cars are started by their own powerful batteries, which first operate an electric starting motor. To keep the engine cool, most models have a water-filled radiator although some rely on air. The driver controls the pulling power of the engine through the gearbox and clutch.

HOW CARS ARE BUILT

We have already seen how mass production techniques revolutionised the manufacture of cars and also how robot machines perform the donkey work nowadays. In a car factory, everything is done strictly in order.

First the body parts are cut from metal sheets and welded together to form a shell. Only after this is painted are the engine and gearbox fitted. Finally, seats, windows and tyres are added, before the car is ready to be driven off to be tested to make sure each part is working. An inspector must give his or her approval before the car is passed on for sale.

New models go through a much more rigorous safety routine. Manufacturers use people-shaped dummies as drivers to see what happens during crashes. Drivers also speed around special tracks to test a vehicle's limitations, ensuring it is absolutely safe before it reaches the streets.

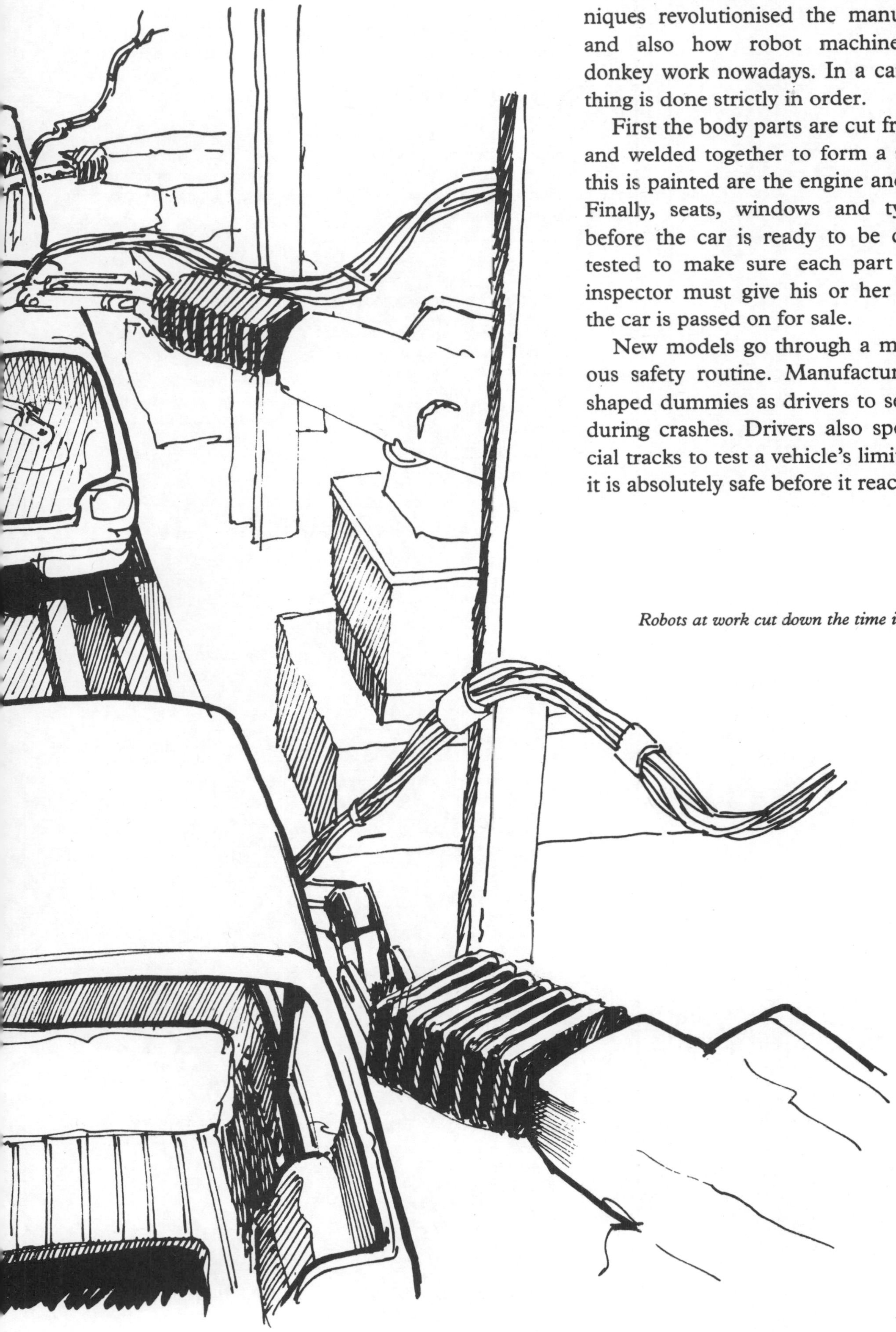

Robots at work cut down the time it takes to make a car.

SPORTS CAR MODELS

You will need an ordinary craft knife with renewable blades, a small pair of scissors and a ball point pen that has run out of ink. Use a small tube of contact adhesive (the sort that goes onto each surface to be stuck and is then left to dry for a few moments before the parts are pressed together). You will also need some ordinary glue to assemble the wheels.

Work in a well lit area where you can leave your model parts without them being damaged. Use a plastic cutting board or a thick piece of cardboard to protect furniture.

Remove the model pages from the book before cutting them to shape. Read the instructions and look at the drawings to ensure you understand the assembly stages before starting to cut the parts. If you are not sure go back over the instructions. Only cut out the parts as you need them in assembly. Cut along the solid black lines, making short cuts up the glue flaps, towards the panels, to help the curved sides take shape. Press just enough to cut through the card and cut slowly.

Crease the dotted lines with the ball point pen, running it along gently to make a mark, and then going over it again to make a deeper crease. Try this on scrap card first to see how it works.

Do not apply glue straight from the tube. Use a strip of thick card as a narrow brush to spread the glue exactly where it is needed on the hatched glue areas. Use these areas to position the parts.

Line up the parts before you begin to assemble them. Take your time, don't rush, and check every step first.

All three model cars share common construction features, such as body formers, curved side panels and doors, and tyre and wheel construction. Take care to curve parts evenly; ensure that everything lines up and that you understand the additional assembly in the Countach.

COUNTACH

STEP 1

Cut out and fold cockpit floor to shape. Cut out left and right body formers and glue to each side of cockpit floor.
Cut out, fold and glue the body tray and rear panel between the body formers as shown.

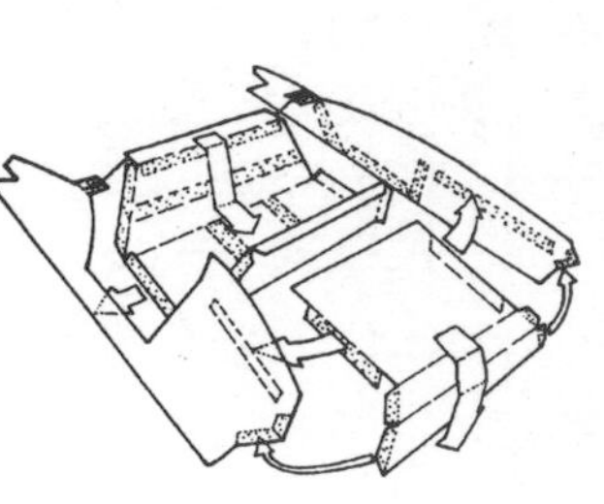

STEP 2

Cut out and curve seat fronts to shape. Note inner and outer parts before assembly. Glue into position.
Now assemble centre console as shown, glue sides of gear lever together and glue into slit in console.
Fold dash panel to shape, tuck in flaps and glue to front bulkhead in position marked.
Cut out and fold instrument panel into shape and glue sides at B.
Now glue into dash panel as shown.
Fold and glue steering column into instrument panel. Glue steering wheel to column.
Note glue positions for centre console on cockpit floor when positioning. Spot glue lower edges of seats and glue either side.

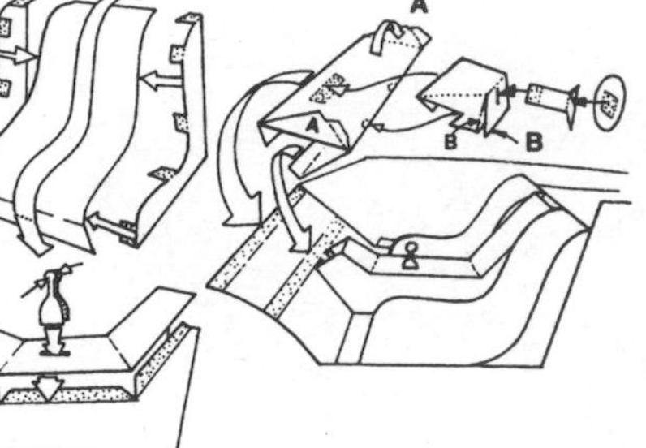

STEP 3

To glue bonnet in position, cut out and fold front edge as shown, curving main panel of bonnet. Glue rear edge underside flap A to front of cockpit at A. Note outer edges overhang. Fold in and glue small front flaps at B.

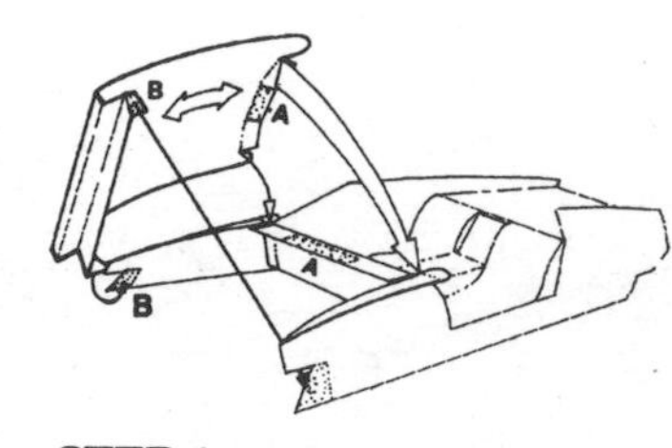

STEP 4

Curve body outer left, and fold in flaps to complete shape. Try this part in position and see how flaps at D glue under bonnet edge, glue this first. Ensure you understand how this part is positioned.
Now glue along flap at A. Glue flaps E, F, C and B – *IN THAT ORDER*

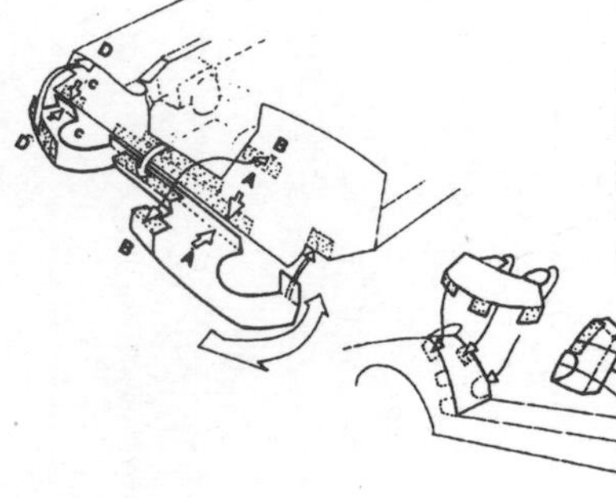

STEP 5

Cut out right side wings and door. Curve the front wing and glue to under bonnet edge at A. Glue flaps E. Curve rear wing and glue B, D and C *IN THAT ORDER.* Curve door, fold to shape and glue flap F, then G, in position. Note how parts locate with door, overlapping wings.

View structure all round and ensure shape matches up, gently squeeze or bend if necessary.

STEP 6

Glue rear body panels into position, outer flap first. Glue air intakes together at front and glue to top of body panels as shown; spot glue front edge arrowed.
Glue roof into position as arrowed at B and side flap A. Roll under flaps C and glue to roof. Glue flaps to body former at D and flaps E to bonnet. Curve and glue wheel arches into positions shown.

STEP 7

Cut out and fold left side door to shape. See how it fits. Now glue door former together and the rounded flap to door as shown. Door raises as arrowed.

Cut out and curve mirrors to shape. Glue flaps as shown, then glue into positions marked on doors.

STEP 8

Cut out rear light. Fold and fit into rear body, gluing flaps B and A.

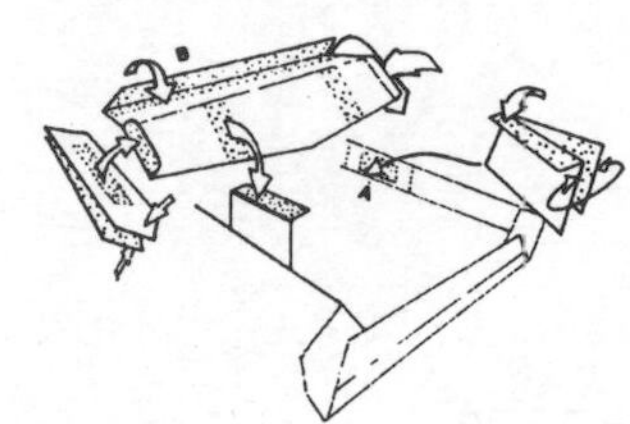

STEP 9

Fold and glue wing struts together and fold down top flap. Glue to inner bodywork at A. Fold over and glue flap on rear wing at B. Fold up rear of wing and fold down end flaps.
Glue wing end plates together.
Glue completed wing centrally to wing struts as arrowed.

STEP 10

Roll tyre strips as shown and glue. Glue wheels and backings together. Stand tyres on their edges and push the wheel discs down inside. Keep tyres pressed onto the work surface and spot glue around edge of wheel. Spot glue tyre into position as arrowed. Trim discs to exact fit.

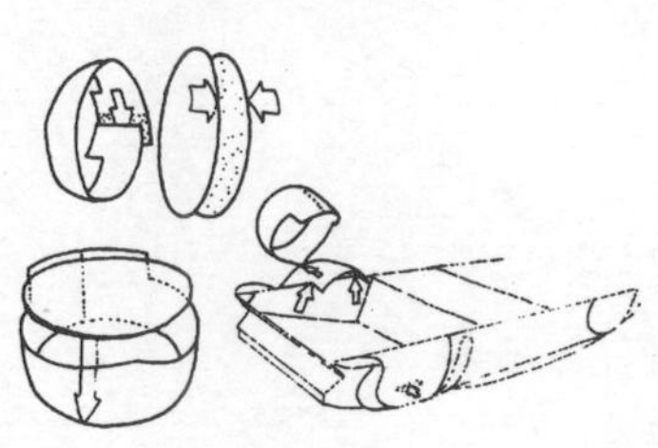

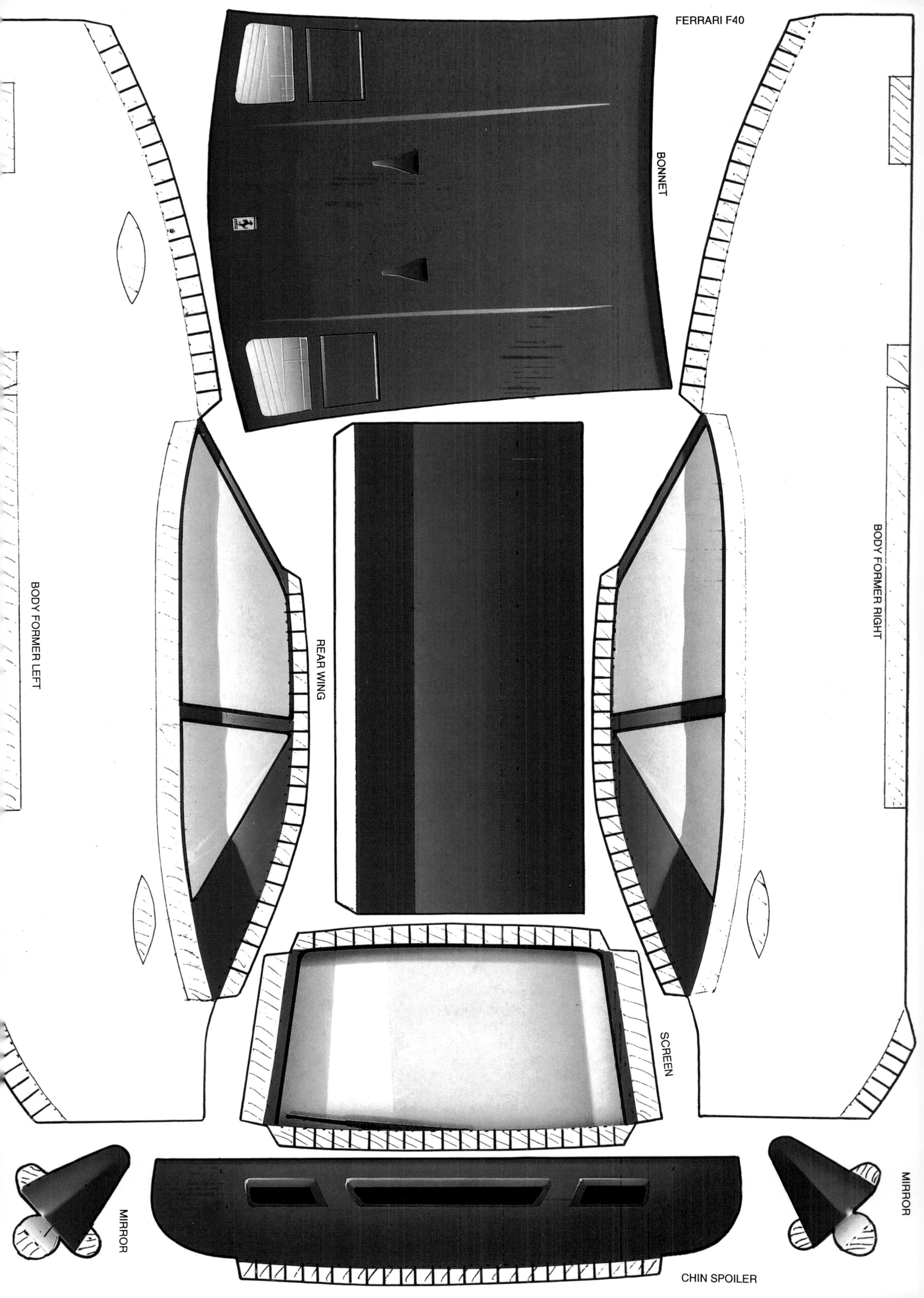
FERRARI F40
BONNET
BODY FORMER LEFT
BODY FORMER RIGHT
REAR WING
SCREEN
MIRROR
MIRROR
CHIN SPOILER

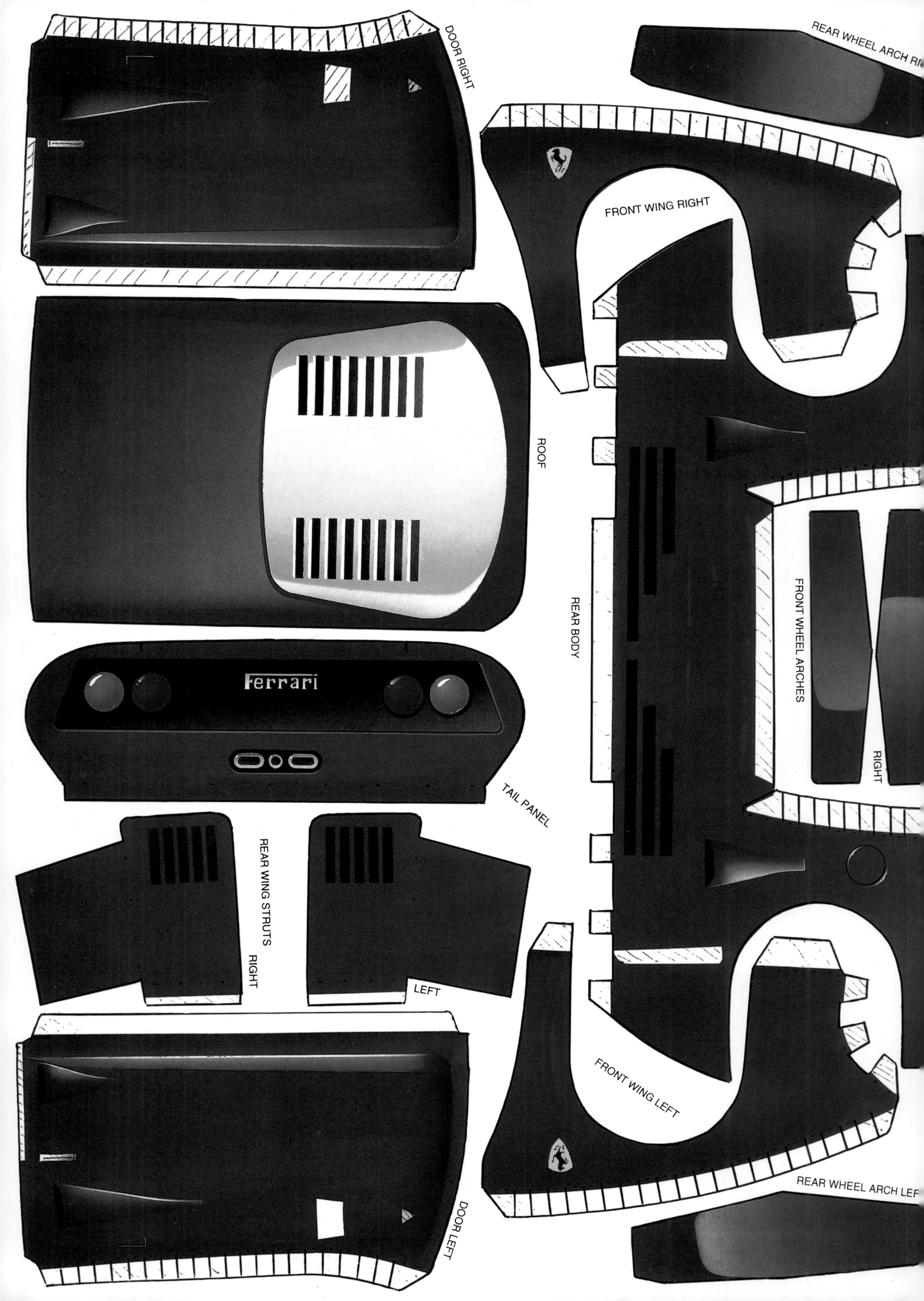

DOOR RIGHT
REAR WHEEL ARCH RI
FRONT WING RIGHT
ROOF
REAR BODY
FRONT WHEEL ARCHES
RIGHT
Ferrari
TAIL PANEL
REAR WING STRUTS
RIGHT
LEFT
FRONT WING LEFT
REAR WHEEL ARCH LEF
DOOR LEFT

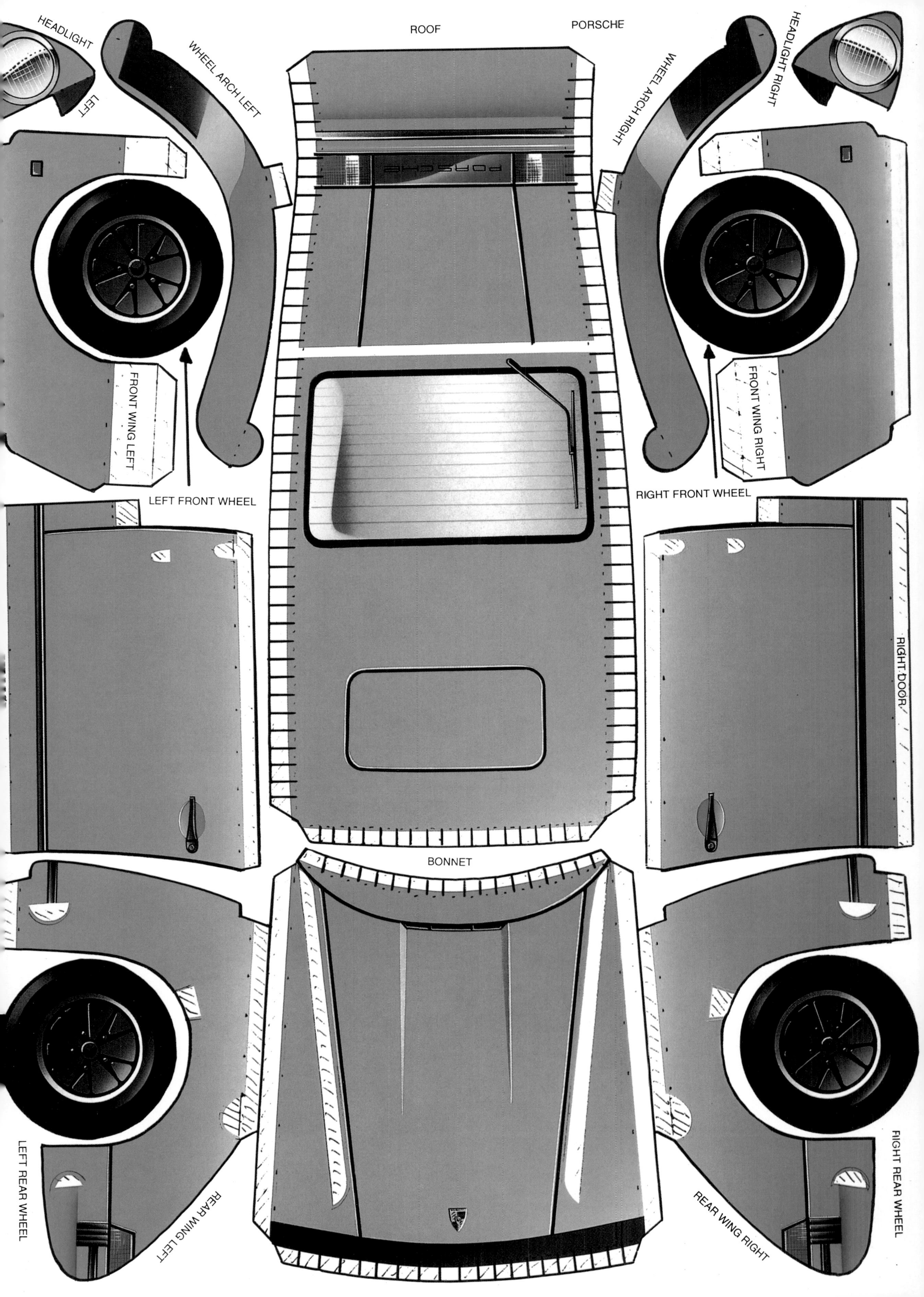

HEADLIGHT LEFT
WHEEL ARCH LEFT
ROOF
PORSCHE
WHEEL ARCH RIGHT
HEADLIGHT RIGHT
FRONT WING LEFT
FRONT WING RIGHT
LEFT FRONT WHEEL
RIGHT FRONT WHEEL
RIGHT DOOR
BONNET
LEFT REAR WHEEL
REAR WING LEFT
REAR WING RIGHT
RIGHT REAR WHEEL

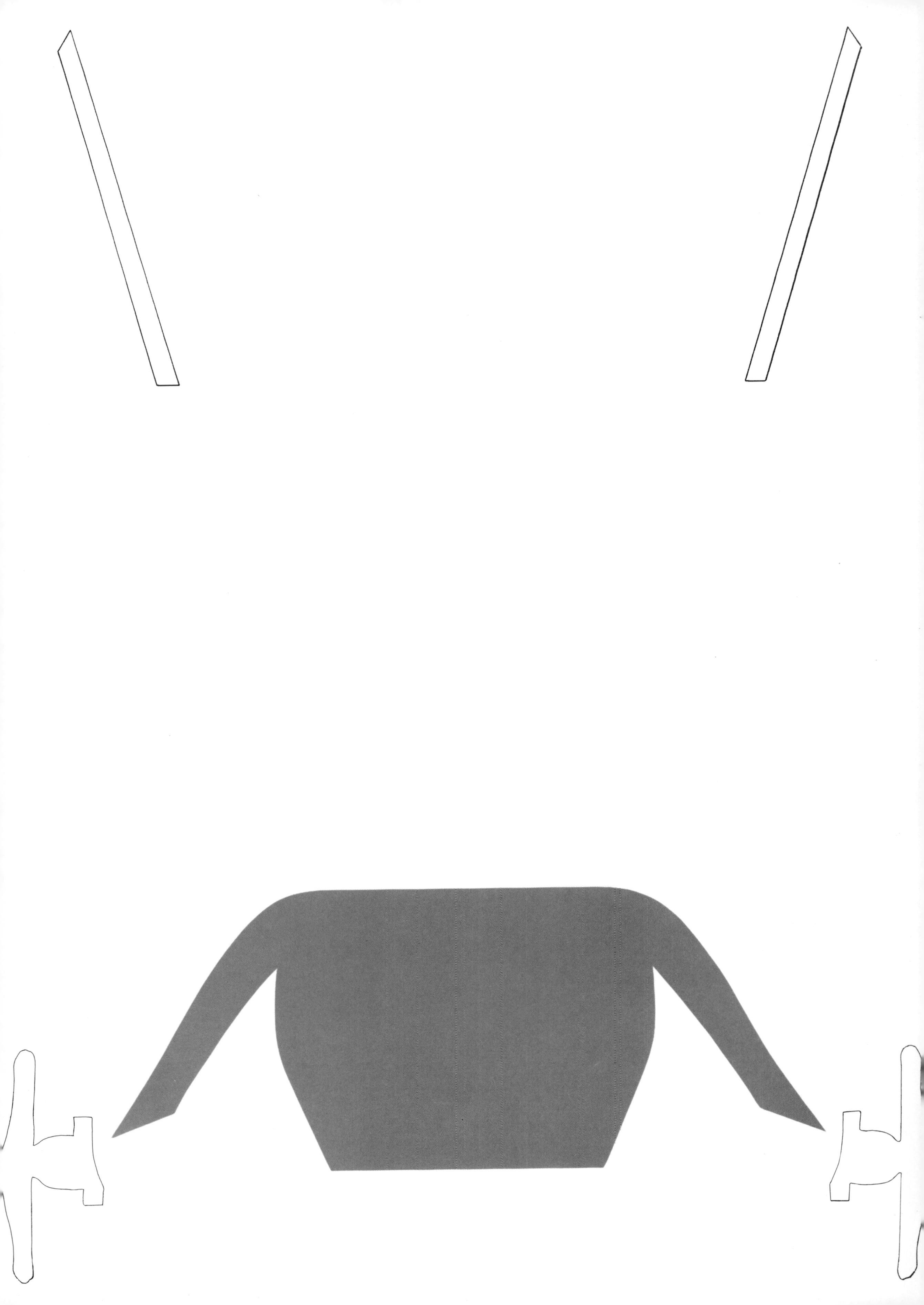

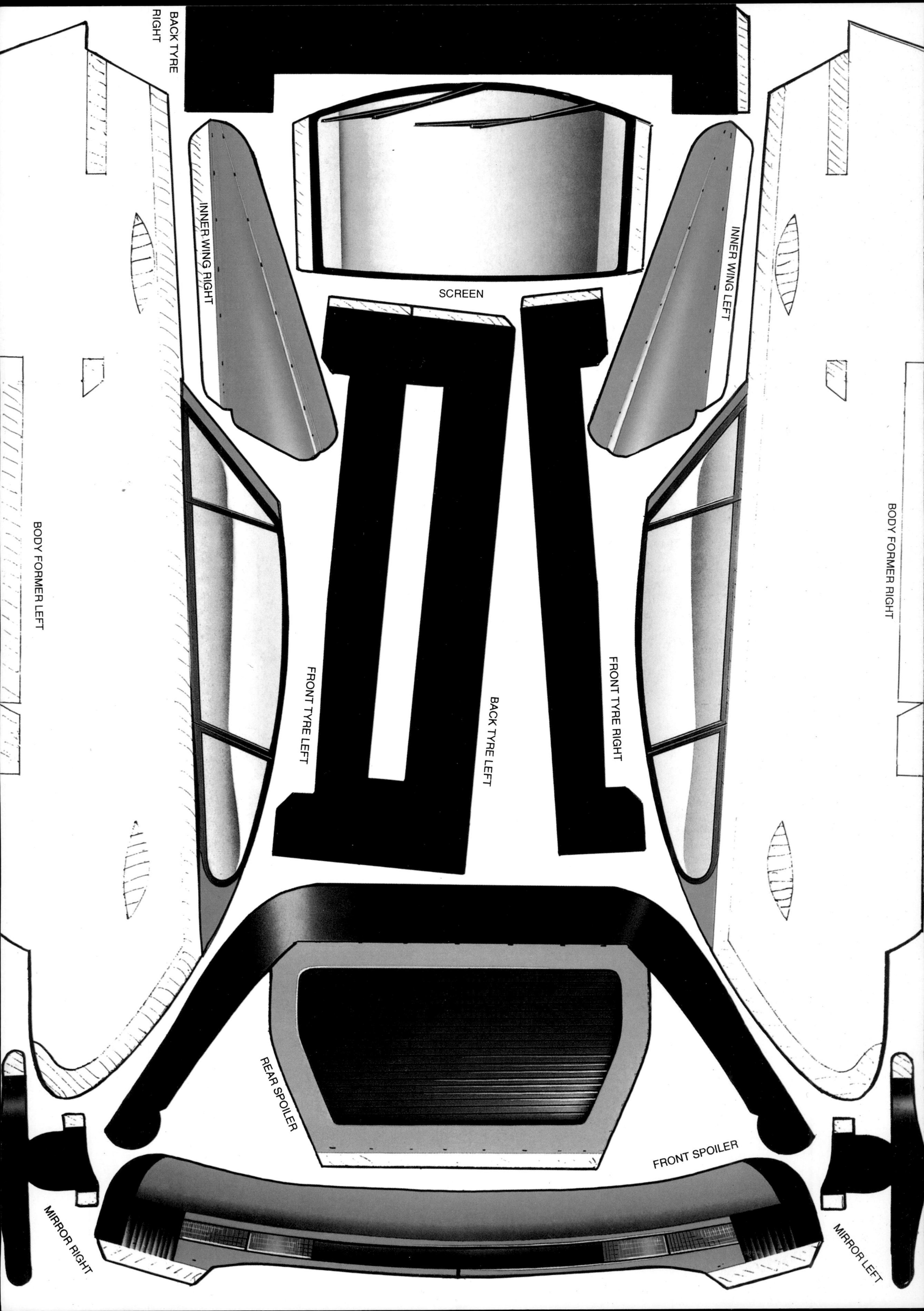
BACK TYRE RIGHT
INNER WING RIGHT
SCREEN
INNER WING LEFT
BODY FORMER LEFT
BODY FORMER RIGHT
FRONT TYRE LEFT
BACK TYRE LEFT
FRONT TYRE RIGHT
REAR SPOILER
FRONT SPOILER
MIRROR RIGHT
MIRROR LEFT

DOOR BACK
BODY SIDE RIGHT
MIRROR RIGHT
MIRROR LEFT
BODY SIDE LEFT
DOOR FRONT
BODY FORMER LEFT
INSTRUMENT PANEL
DOOR LEFT
WING END PLATE
BODY TRAY AND REAR PANEL
BODY FORMER RIGHT
countach
RIGHT SEAT INNER
GEAR LEVER
GEAR LEVER
LEFT SEAT INNER

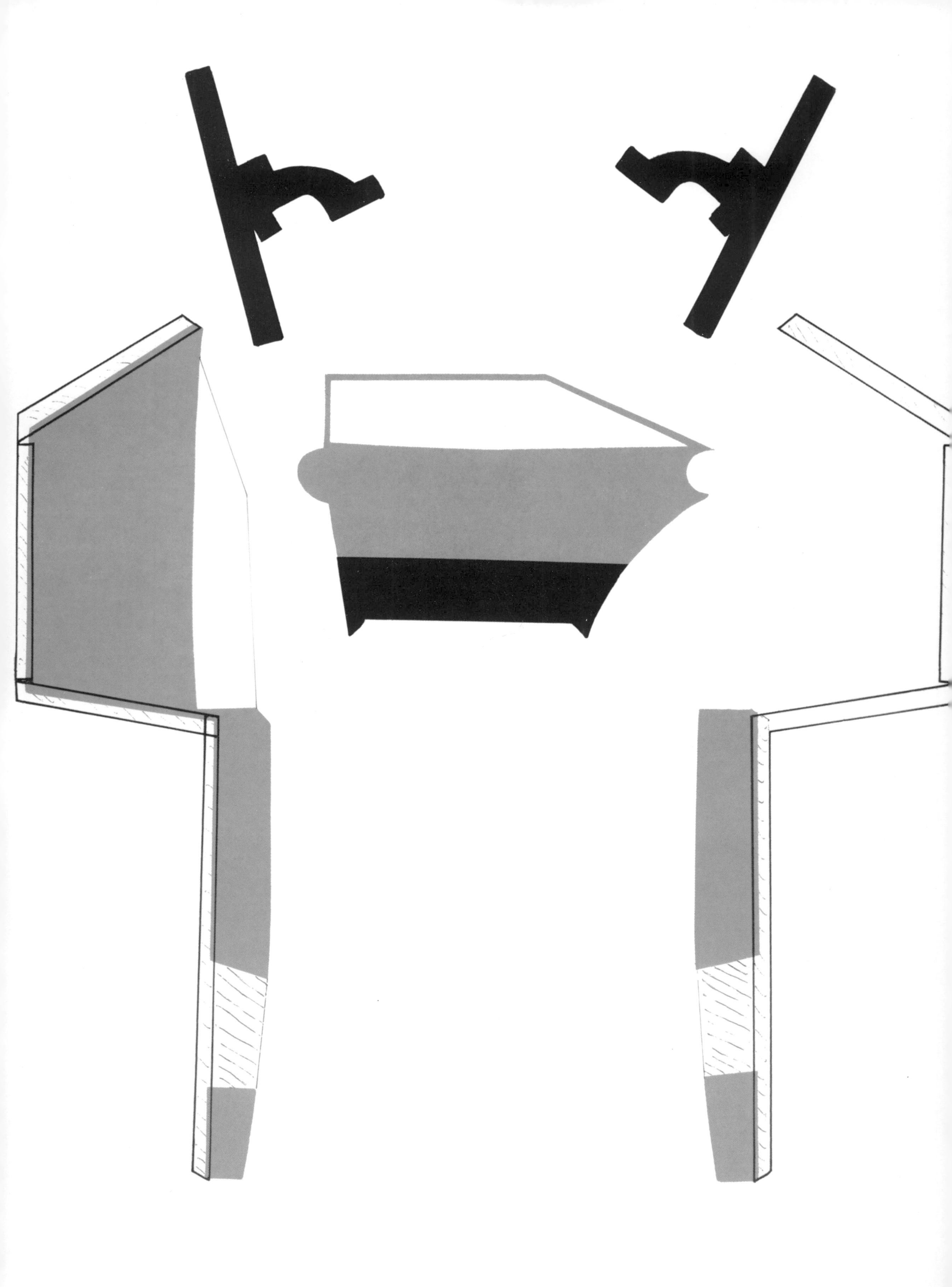

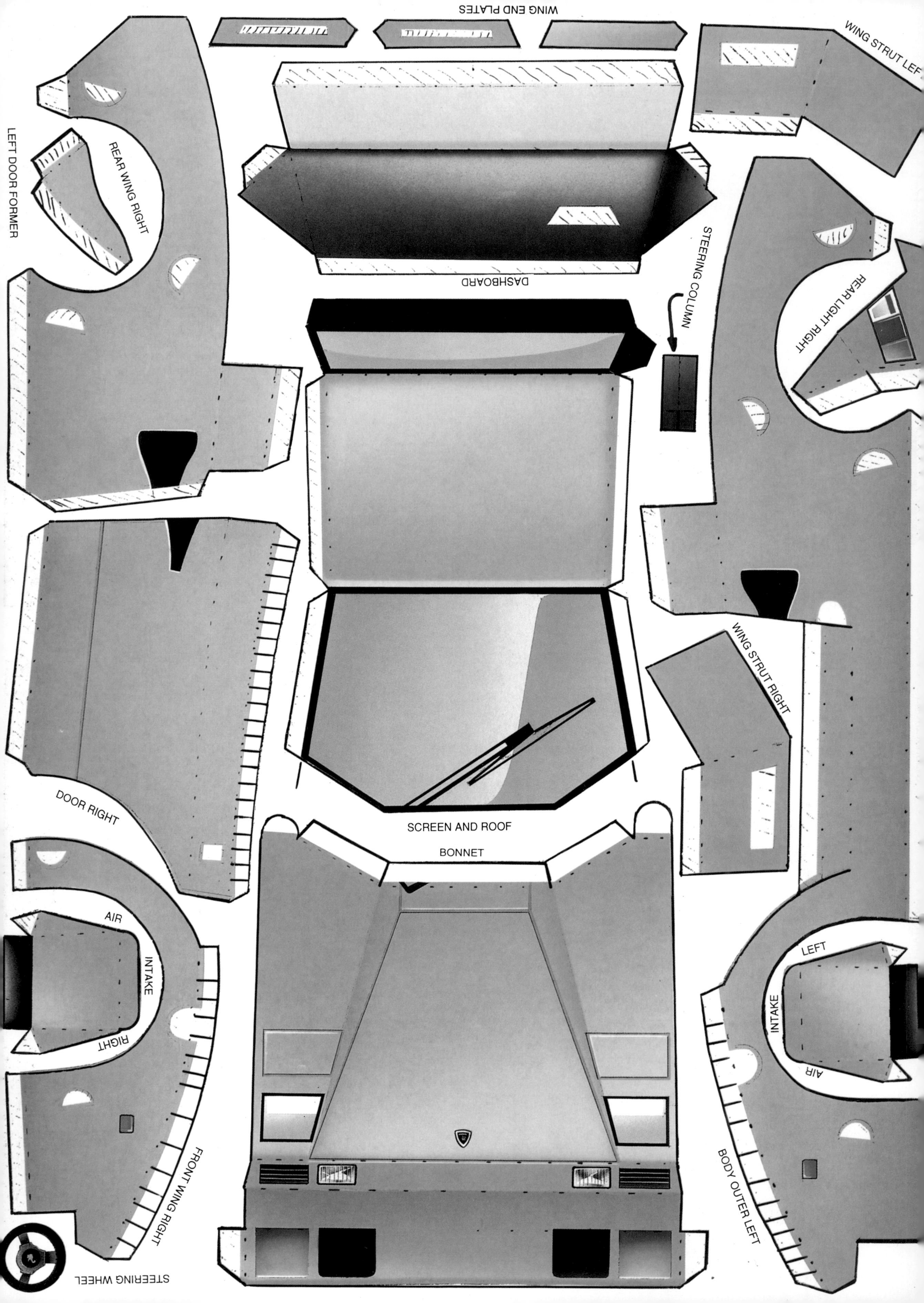

WING END PLATES
WING STRUT LEFT
LEFT DOOR FORMER
REAR WING RIGHT
DASHBOARD
STEERING COLUMN
REAR LIGHT RIGHT
WING STRUT RIGHT
DOOR RIGHT
SCREEN AND ROOF
BONNET
AIR
INTAKE
RIGHT
LEFT
INTAKE
AIR
FRONT WING RIGHT
BODY OUTER LEFT
STEERING WHEEL

FRONT TYRE RIGHT
FRONT TYRE LEFT
BACK TYRE RIGHT
BACK TYRE LEFT
BACK WHEELS
COUNTACH
COUNTACH
COUNTACH
REAR WING
FERRARI F40
FRONT TYRE RIGHT
BACK TYRE RIGHT
REAR WHEELS
WHEEL BACKINGS ARE MARKED *
FRONT WHEELS
BACK TYRE LEFT
FRONT TYRE LEFT

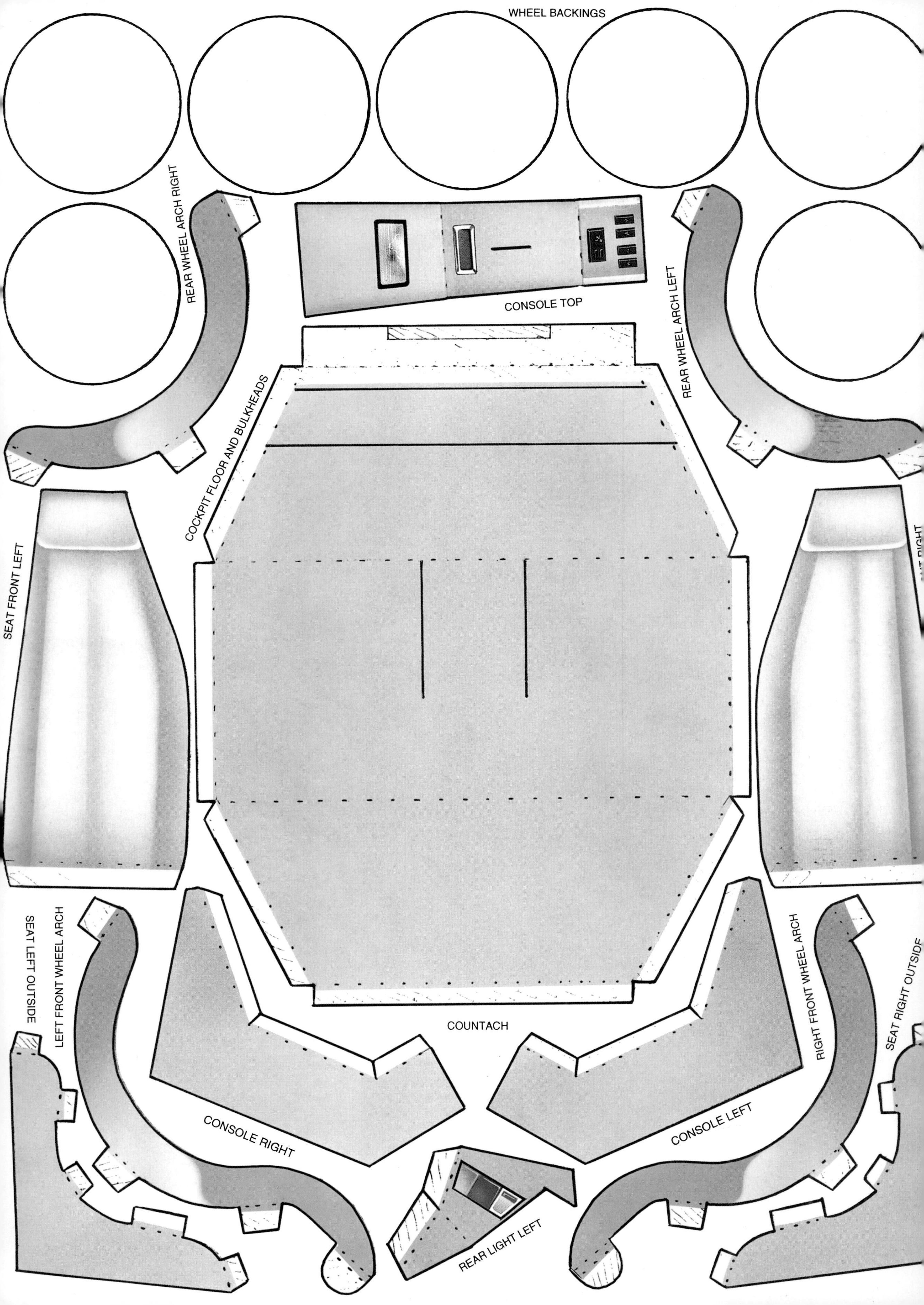
WHEEL BACKINGS
REAR WHEEL ARCH RIGHT
CONSOLE TOP
REAR WHEEL ARCH LEFT
COCKPIT FLOOR AND BULKHEADS
SEAT FRONT LEFT
SEAT LEFT OUTSIDE
LEFT FRONT WHEEL ARCH
COUNTACH
RIGHT FRONT WHEEL ARCH
SEAT RIGHT OUTSIDE
CONSOLE RIGHT
CONSOLE LEFT
REAR LIGHT LEFT

N.B.
'SPOT GLUING' = APPLY A SPOT OF GLUE WITH A STRIP OF THICK CARDBOARD.

FERRARI

STEP 1

Cut out screen, bonnet and roof and curve to shape. Glue in position. Note how door overlaps wing.

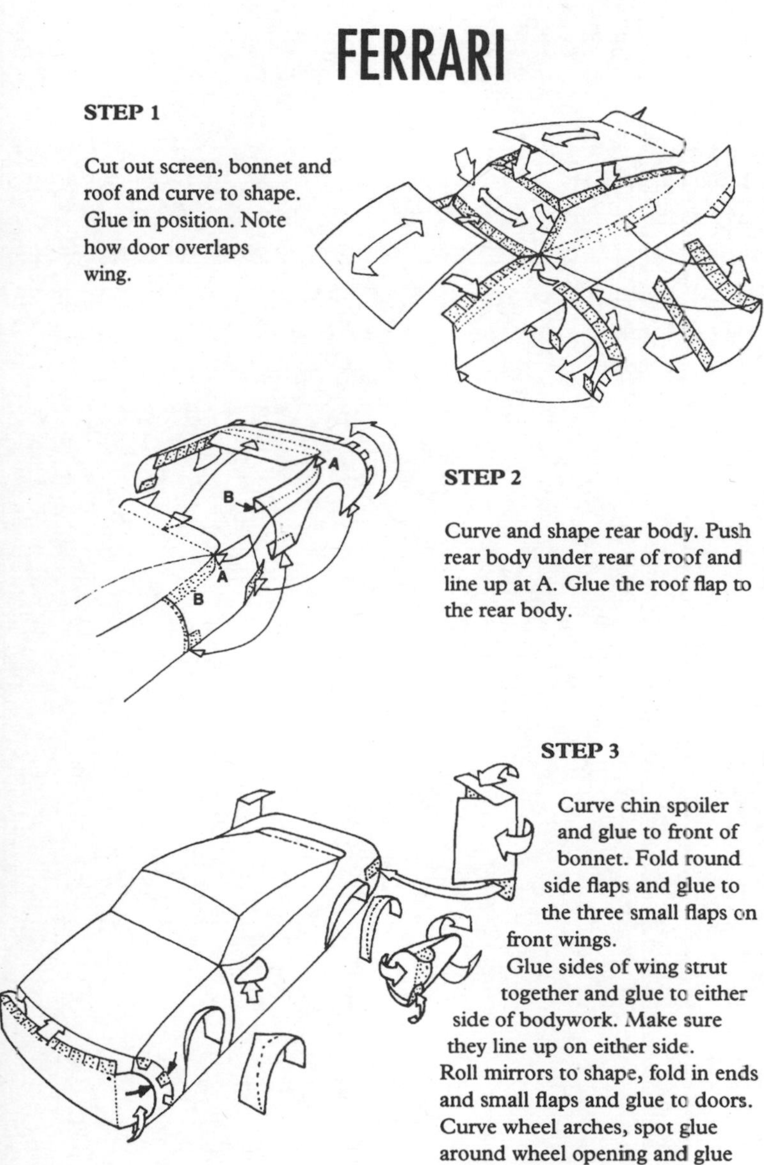

STEP 2

Curve and shape rear body. Push rear body under rear of roof and line up at A. Glue the roof flap to the rear body.

STEP 3

Curve chin spoiler and glue to front of bonnet. Fold round side flaps and glue to the three small flaps on front wings.
Glue sides of wing strut together and glue to either side of bodywork. Make sure they line up on either side.
Roll mirrors to shape, fold in ends and small flaps and glue to doors.
Curve wheel arches, spot glue around wheel opening and glue arch to edges of wing.

STEP 4

Fold rear wing to shape and glue along flap as shown. Glue flaps in wing struts into ends of wing. Glue rear panel onto flaps on rear body. Fold under lower flap stiffener.

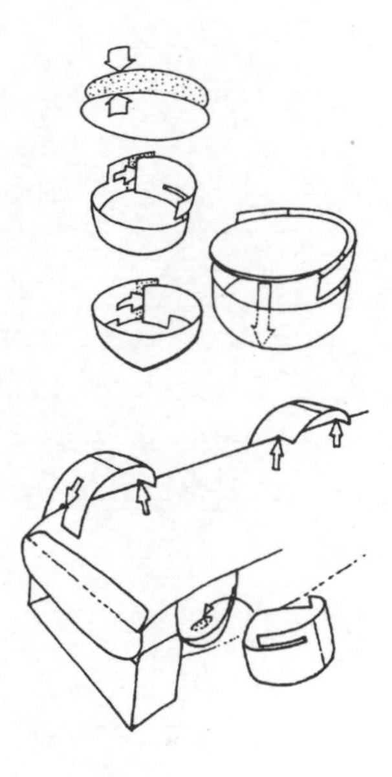

STEP 5

Roll tyre strips as shown and glue. Glue wheels and backings together.
Stand tyres on their outer edges and push wheel discs down inside. Keep tyre pressed onto the work surfaces and spot glue around edge of wheel.

Spot glue tyres in position as shown. Note how rears slot over body sides.

PORSCHE

STEP 1

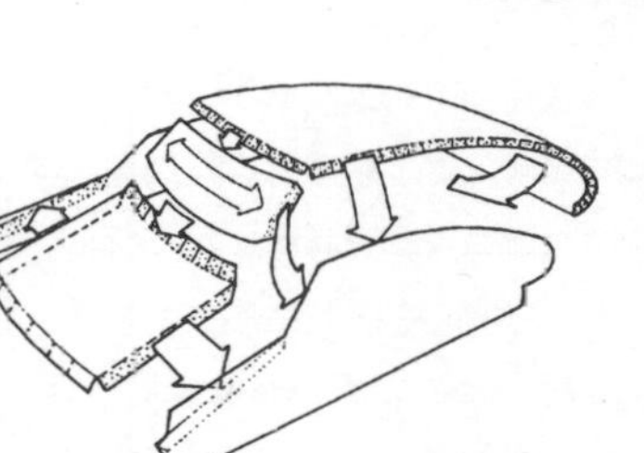

Cut out screen and bonnet and glue together. Then glue completed assembly to body formers as shown.
Cut out and curve roof, more at rear, and glue to edges of body formers, bringing under the rear edge to complete the body shape.

STEP 2

Curve front inner wings and glue one side to positions on bonnet as arrowed at B. Crease glue flap on other side and glue to outside of body former at A with crease running along top edge of body former. Ensure both inner wings are curved to match. Try them in position first.
Curve front and rear wing and door for right and left sides. See how they position on the body formers, using the glue positions as a guide.
Glue front wing in position as shown, glue door in position, lower edge first, and overlap front wing. Glue small flap at front of door to the wing underside.
Tuck rear wing under rear edge of door and glue in position along top edge and rear curve, then glue lower flap in position.
Assemble mirrors. Glue curved strips to flaps C and then glue rounded flaps to doors.

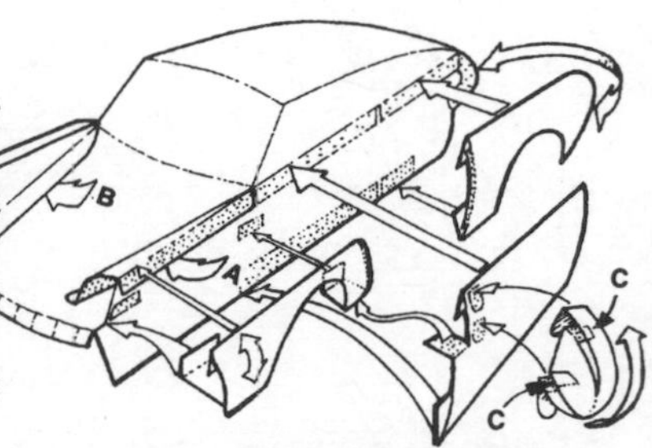

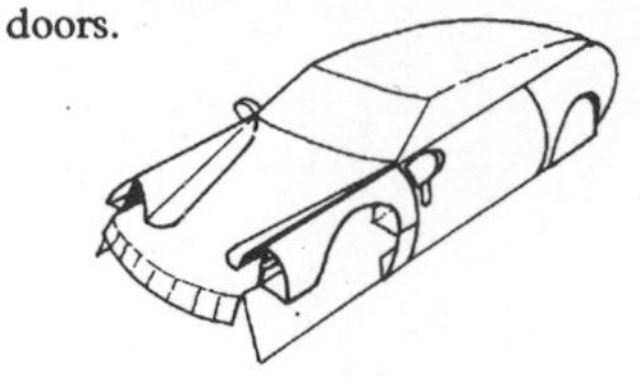

STEP 3

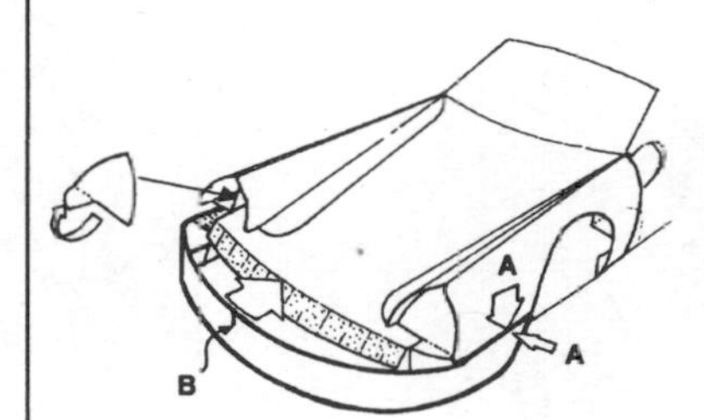

Curve front spoiler and glue to front of bonnet and to underside of front wings at A.
Note centre mark on front spoiler arrowed.

STEP 4

Roll tyre strips as shown and glue. Glue wheels and backings together. Then stand tyres on their outer edges and push the wheel discs down inside. Keep the tyre pressed onto the work surface and spot glue around the edge of wheel.
Spot glue tyre into position as arrowed.

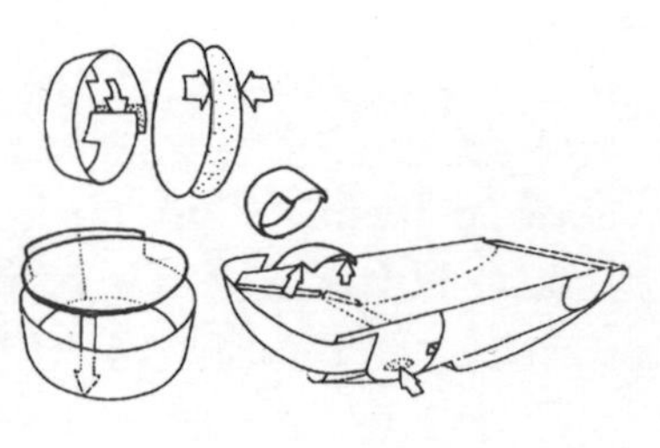

STEP 5

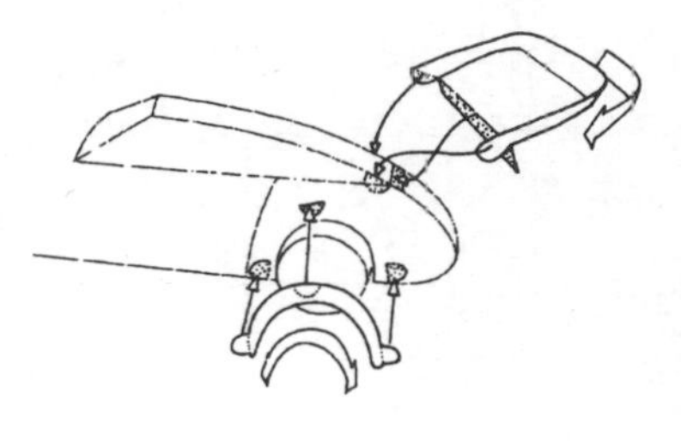

Curve rear wheel arches, fold centre glue flap over and glue flaps into position as arrowed.
Curve sides of rear wing, form shape and glue long flap to rear bodywork and side flaps in position arrowed

SAFETY ON THE ROADS

Today's cars are safer to drive than ever before. Manufacturers now rate safety factors as highly as performance and petrol consumption.

There are two levels of safety features. Primary safety includes roadholding, braking, steering and handling and helps prevent accidents. Secondary safety includes air bags, collapsible steering wheels and side bars which help you survive accidents when they happen. The first batch are more vital because it is far better to prevent the accident happening in the first place.

Air bags: Air bags are tucked into the steering wheel and inflate like a huge balloon within a split second of an impact. Many injuries are caused when the driver's body hits the steering wheel. With an air-filled bag between the two, the driver is protected. They are particularly effective in head-on collisions.

Windscreen wipers: Clear vision is vital for the safety of drivers. The first mechanical windscreen wipers appeared on cars in 1910.

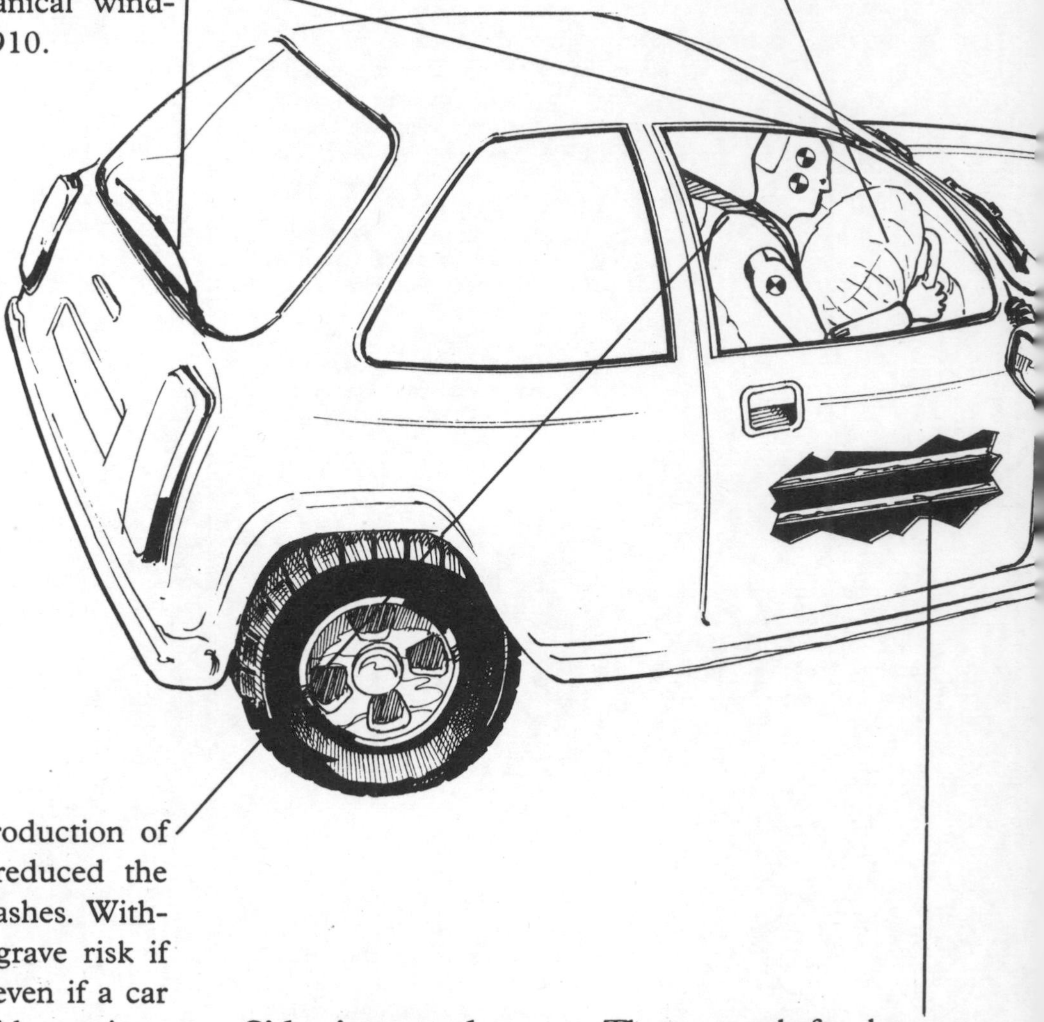

Safety belts: The compulsory introduction of safety belts in Britain drastically reduced the number of people killed in road smashes. Without seat belts, passengers were at grave risk if there was a crash. That is because even if a car stops after a collision, the people inside continue to travel at speed. Belts are designed to counteract this effect, called *inertia,* by securing passengers in their seats following an impact.

Side impact beams: These are hefty bars inserted into the doors of cars, which give extra protection to drivers and passengers in side-on collisions. This is the most common kind of crash.

8 CARS WHICH STARRED ON SCREEN

Chitty Chitty Bang Bang, the star of a 1968 film starring Dick Van Dyke and Benny Hill about an inventor who renovates a car and gives it amazing abilities.

The *Batmobile* featured as the faithful carriage of hero Batman and his sidekick Robin in the American TV series and the film version made in 1966.

The Yellow Rolls Royce was the title of a 1964 film which told three stories about the ill-fated owners of the grand car.

Herbie, otherwise known as *The Love Bug,* was the Volkswagen with a mind of its own which starred in four films made in the Seventies.

American Graffiti, made in 1973, became a hit film not so much for its array of stars in the cast but for the classic American cars they drove.

Smokey and the Bandit was a box office smash after it was released in 1977 to audiences who relished seeing spectacular car crashes – in which nobody was hurt – in a lengthy, comical police chase.

James Bond had a series of incredible machines in the series of 007 which began in 1962.

Genevieve is the name of the 1953 film and the vintage car which gets into some friendly rivalry on its return from the London to Brighton veterans' rally.

Traffic lights: The familiar red, amber and green lights are immensely important for controlling vehicles. Without them there would be chaos on our roads. The first were lit up in Detroit, USA, in 1919.

Cats' eyes: You'll find these small, reflective, spongy buttons down the centre of roads or across junctions. First invented in 1935, they enable drivers to follow the line of the carriageway as the 'eyes' light up in the beam of car headlamps. They cost next to nothing to install and are easy to maintain, but provide a huge boost to safe driving after dark.

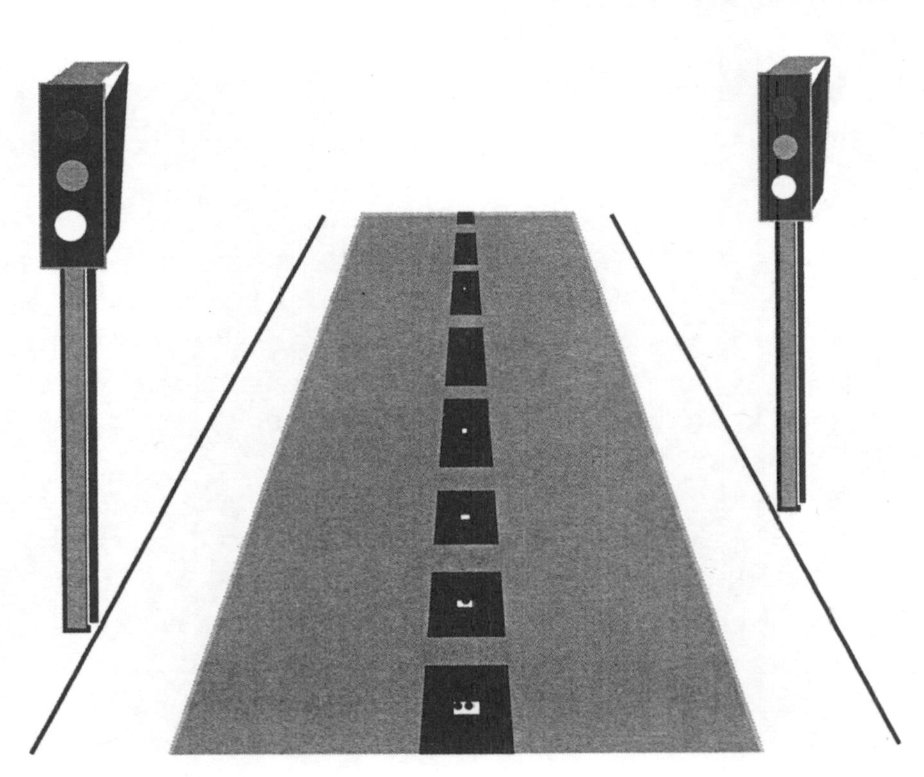

FAMOUS CAR MODELS

MINI

The inspiration for the first Mini was the world oil crisis in 1956. Designer Leonard Lord realised there was a huge demand for a small car which was cheap to run. Virtually the only choice on the market at the time was the Bubble Car, which most people considered to be a glorified motor cycle.

The design of the Mini was the work of Alex Issigonis, the man behind the famous Morris Minor shape. The British public first caught a glimpse of the Mini in August 1959. Although small, it had four seats because the wheels were placed in the corners to give maximum room to the interior. The engine was also mounted sideways. The four millionth model rolled off the production lines in November 1976.

Austin Mini.

CADILLAC

The Cadillac car company was formed on 21 August 1901 in Detroit. It was named after the French explorer Antoine de la Mothe Cadillac. The first model ever produced was sold in Buffalo, New York State, in October, the following year. But it wasn't to stay independent for long. By 1909 it had been swallowed up by the giant American General Motors Group. But the name was kept alive and, thanks to the hard work of salesman-cum-executive Alfred P. Sloan, who took over the group in 1923, Cadillac went on to become the last word in status cars. Its large, gas-guzzling engine proved no problem to feed in oil-rich America. In their heyday, Cadillacs were set apart from their rivals with trimmings of shiny chrome plating, huge tail fins, wire wheels and open tops. Top Hollywood stars of the image-conscious Fifties refused to be seen in anything else.

E-Type Jaguar.

JAGUAR

The man behind the Jaguar car company was William Lyons, who began his career in the motor industry in 1922 making and selling motorcycle sidecars. Soon his Swallow Sidecar Company turned its talents to making car bodies and did well.

Moving from its Blackpool base to Coventry in 1928, it began to produce cars complete with engines. Its first model was an *SS1* which at £300 was an outstanding success. The first Jaguar came onto the market in 1935, taking the name of the sleek, graceful jungle cat known for its speed.

Probably its best known and most loved model was the Jaguar E-Type, unleashed on the public in 1961. With a top speed of 240 km (150 miles) per hour and a long, pouting nose, the E-Type was as slick as any other sports car available at the time, but a fraction of the price. For example, at little more than £2,000, the Jaguar was

An American jeep.

one third of the price of an equivalent Ferrari. In 1966, Lyons's company, by now known as Jaguar, merged with the British Motor Company and both soon became known as British Leyland.

William Lyons received a knighthood for his services to the British motor industry. When he retired he was replaced by the dynamic John Egan, who was at the helm when Jaguar resumed its status of an independent company. Recently Jaguar has been taken over by Ford along with another prestige sports car brand, Aston Martin.

JEEP

This is the name for four-wheel drive military motors, which first went by the name 'General Purpose' vehicle. This title was eventually shortened to jeep. As a combat vehicle, it has to be tough and sturdy to withstand demanding conditions.

Jeeps have special features which make them a valuable asset to any army. The windscreen folds flat to protect it under fire. Heavy duty tyres have deep treads which can grip to all sorts of surfaces, like mud, sand and snow. A special arrangement of gears helps the driver to keep control of the vehicle in these extreme conditions. It boasts a capacity of a quarter of a ton when the seats are taken out so it is not only handy for carrying troops but also ferrying supplies. Soldiers also make use of it for towing equipment like guns.

ELECTRIC CAR

Vehicles driven by electricity – like milk floats, invalid cars and golf buggies – have one big plus. They don't use petrol so they don't create pollution. But the downside of the battery-powered machine is that it won't go very far or very fast. It will need recharging regularly, which makes long journeys impractical. Milk floats are charged up every night. Their speed amounts to little more than 16 km (10 miles) per hour. British police have road-tested an electric three-wheeled police patrol car called the ZEV. Costing £13,000 each, they manage a top speed of 64 km (40 miles) per hour and can run for 96 km (60 miles) or 16 hours before needing a charge-up. Forces are earmarking the patrol car for use on street beats and in car parks. Similar motors are used by officers in New York.

Formula One racing car.

RACING CAR

Watch TV coverage of Grand Prix motor races around the world, and you will immediately see the difference between top performance racing cars and familiar family saloons and hatchbacks. Racing cars are specially designed to reach speeds of more than 322 km (200 miles) per hour on the track. To achieve this the cars have a nose that bows low, a cockpit-style seat in front of the engine and a taller back flap, vital for maintaining the car's balance. Racing cars have four wide wheels which are smooth or treadless in dry weather. Melting rubber on the wheel helps to keep the car on the track. Only in wet weather are treads used. The Formula One cars driven by racing heroes like Nigel Mansell, Ayrton Senna and Alain Prost are so advanced they have computers tucked into the design to report back on performance. But still they rely on flags throughout the race for important information. A blue flag means a car is close behind, while a red and yellow flag warns of a slippery road.

All drivers hope to see the black and white chequered flag waved when the winner crosses the finishing line, but an all-black flag tells the driver either his manoeuvres or his car are a danger. If anything goes wrong on the track the driver can pull off into a pit, where a team of 14 skilled mechanics will change all four wheels and have the car back on the road in just eight seconds.

LIMOUSINE

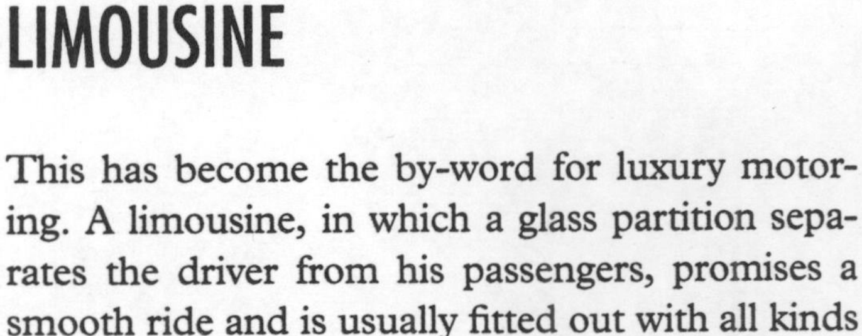

This has become the by-word for luxury motoring. A limousine, in which a glass partition separates the driver from his passengers, promises a smooth ride and is usually fitted out with all kinds of little extras; top grade upholstery on the seats, tinted glass, bullet-proofing and even a built-in drinks cabinet. In America, the ultimate in limousines is a 'stretch limo', where there is even more splendour and opulence. The world's longest car is a super-stretch limousine measuring 30.5 m (99 feet) long. It takes no less than 26 wheels to keep this monster on the road and the fittings include a waterbed and small swimming pool.

In the future solar powered cars may look like this.

SOLAR CAR

The vehicle of tomorrow is probably the solar car, which runs on energy converted from the sun's rays. The most successful are hallmarked by a futuristic shape with a pointed rear end and nose like a small aeroplane.

The solar panels are on the back and look like sheets of black glass. In fact they are cells, about 8,000 in number, which give an output of some 1,550 watts – about enough to power 25 lightbulbs. Latest speed trials have produced the most encouraging results yet. These days solar cars can travel at up to 80 km (50 miles) per hour, far outstripping earlier performances, without giving off one puff of poisonous emissions. A special plastic hood with gold-plating keeps the sun's rays from the inside of the car.

SOME MODERN FACTS ABOUT CARS

The longest road in the world is the Pan American Highway which stretches almost the length of South America.

The world land speed record for a car stands at 1,019 km (633 miles) per hour, faster than many aeroplanes. It was achieved by the golden-colour *Thrust 2* in 1983, with Richard Noble at the controls. The secret of its success was an aircraft jet engine.

For cars without the benefit of a mega-powerful aircraft engine, the speed record stands at 650 km (403.1 miles) per hour. This was set by Donald Campbell's *Bluebird* back in 1964.

The first car to break the 100 km per hour (62 miles) per hour barrier was the battery-driven *La Jamais Contente*. The bullet-shaped car was the talk of France when driver Belgian Camille Jenatzy roared into the record books in 1899.

CAR SECURITY

More than a quarter of all crimes committed in Britain are related to cars, either broken into or stolen. To try to lessen the risk of theft, many gadgets have been devised to help the car owner. Crook locks, strong bars which clasp around the steering wheel and the clutch to prevent the car being driven away; car alarms that emit a loud noise to alert the owner of the car or passers-by that an unauthorised person is opening the car; and registration numbers etched into windows, so thieves are unable to change the identity of the car once it has been stolen. Meanwhile, manufacturers are coming up with better locking systems than ever before.

ECOLOGY

In the past 30 years, the number of motor cars on the roads has soared and it's expected to double again by the year 2025. Their popularity is causing a headache for environmentalists, concerned at the effect on our natural world, because more cars need more roads.

When roads are built, vast areas of natural beauty are dug up to provide the necessary building materials. Unfortunately, it seems big new roads only encourage more car owners to use them and they remain as congested as ever.

Exhaust fumes are unpleasant and smelly, and contain harmful carbon dioxide and other 'greenhouse' gases. Many scientists believe the earth's climate is being threatened by global warming; a problem caused by rising pollution, such as excessive amounts of carbon dioxide in the atmosphere. A car produces about four times its own weight of carbon dioxide in a year.

Another set of gases, nitrogen oxides, are produced when fossil fuels like oil are burnt. These destroy buildings, forests and pond life when they fall as acid rain. Nearly half the nitrogen oxides causing this damage come from road traffic.

The only way to cut pollution is to curb the use of cars. It will mean a big investment in railways and bus services to bring down the cost of travelling, but it is possible to do. In Holland, which was clogged up with cars, the government is aiming to double the number of passengers on its railways. If you travel there on a Sunday afternoon, you will find the trains bursting with passengers, who would rather hop on one of the regular train services than jump in the car.

Traffic calming schemes – like road humps – are another device to cut the misuse of roads by cars. Vehicles which travel more slowly give off less fumes.

Diesel cars and those using unleaded petrol are much cleaner. The most environmentally friendly cars are fitted with a catalytic converter which reduces some of the waste gases from the exhaust pipe.

This is a P[3] Book. This edition published in 2002. P[3], Queen Street House, 4 Queen Street, Bath BA1 1HE, UK.
Cover Design by Starry Dog Books. ISBN 0-75259-221-1. Printed in Malaysia.